I AM THE
THIRSTY
DESERT

DARCY PATTISON

illustrated by

Jordan Kim

Mims House
1309 Broadway
Little Rock, AR 72202
USA

MimsHouseBooks.com

Publisher's Cataloging-in-Publication data

Names: Pattison, Darcy, author. | Kim, Jordan, illustrator.
Title: I am the thirsty desert / Darcy Pattison, illustrated by Jordan
Kim.
Description: Little Rock, AR: Mims House, 2022. | Summary: When
a sudden downpour, a monsoon, falls in the desert, plants and
animals explode with growth.
Identifiers: ISBN: 9781629441771 (hardcover) | 9781629441788
(paperback) | 9781629441795 (ebook) | 9781629441801 (audio) |
LCCN: 2022916331
Subjects: LCSH Desert ecology--Juvenile literature. | Desert
plants--Juvenile literature. | Desert animals--Juvenile literature.
| Monsoons--Juvenile fiction. | BISAC JUVENILE NONFICTION
/ Science & Nature / Environmental Science & Ecosystems |
JUVENILE NONFICTION / Science & Nature / Earth Sciences /
Weather | JUVENILE NONFICTION / Science & Nature / Flowers
& Plants
Classification: LCC QH541.5.D4 P38 2022 | DDC 574.5/2652--
dc23

I am the thirsty desert,

dusty
and parched.

Heat waves build,
swell and sweep,
shimmer and simmer,
across my lands.
I burn.

Water,
I y–e–a–r–n for you.

Monsoon,
I w–a–i–t for you ...

as I cradle a hope
deep
within
my sands.

One day, thunderheads gather.
The monsoon
spills and thrills,
stomps and tromps,
until . . .

...it escapes
to the distant
hills,
where clouds start
to thin,
scatter,
and slip away.

Sweet water puddles
below my cacti,

while a rainbow arcs
the sky,
a glowing halo
glimmering
in the lazy, hazy air.

The monsoon
has sprouted my seeds!
They crack open,
sending
thirsty
roots

wiggling,

niggling,

giggling,

toward fresh water.

At daylight,
the seeds shoot up
to greet . . .

...the heat.

I cannot
stop—
the drying out.
The plants' lives will be brief—
only a day
    or two
        or maybe three—
before they sleep again.

Don't waste this time!   Grow.

Grow.

Grow!

That first day,
sprouts thrust upward,
jostling and jiggling,
straining and stretching
for the w-i-d-e,
w-i-d-e sky,
and by the next day,
under the blazing sun,
plants bud
and blossom,
bursting my
hardpan heart,
until . . .

...I'm flooded with **redbluegreenyelloworangepurple** and buzzing with life—

gorgeous,

outrageous,

fragrant,

frail
LIFE!

But as the afternoon
heats up,
dries up,
disintegrates,

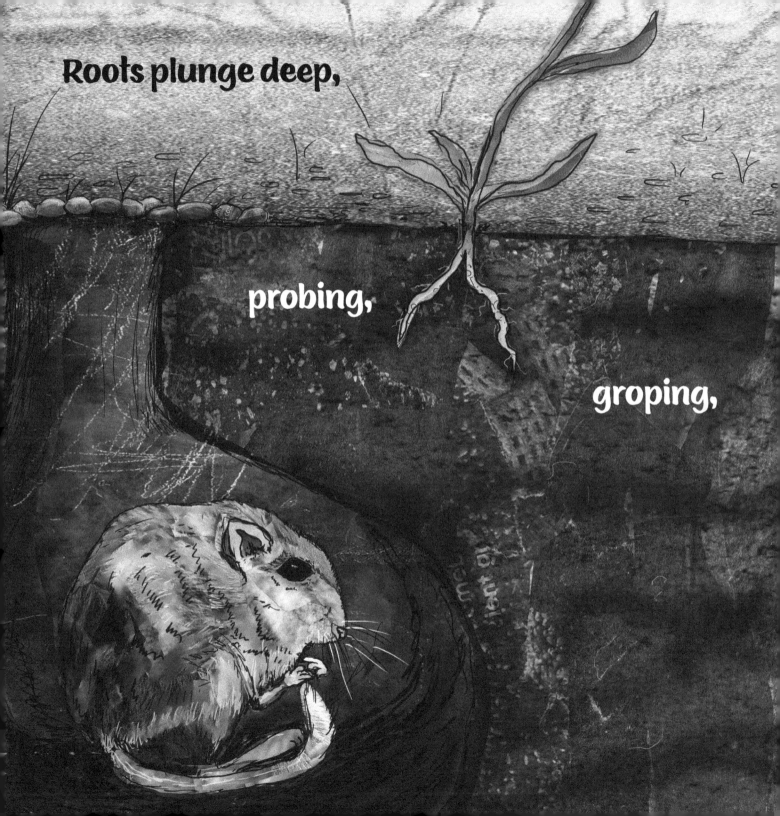

The next day—
a blistering desert day—
flowers droop,

dwindle,

dry,

die.

One day they bloomed, a single day,
a rare day—already yesterday.

And yet—
my bone-dry breeze

rattles and scatters
the sturdy seeds,
flinging them

And then we wait: seeds wait,

I am the thirsty desert,
Dusty and parched.
But I cradle
a hope
deep
within my sands.

I wait,
  I wait,
    I wait ...
   for a quickening storm
     to stomp my way.

DESERT

DESERT – This story takes place in the Sonoran Desert in the southwestern United States and includes plants and animals from that habitat.

A desert is a place that receives little rainfall each year, often less than 10 inches (25 cm). Some deserts are hot and dry, like Death Valley or the Mojave Desert in North America. But there are also cold and dry deserts, such as the Antarctic. In South America, the Atacama Desert of Chile is a coastal desert. Although it is near the sea, it still receives little rain. Some deserts are semiarid, with up to 20 inches (50 cm) of annual rainfall. Deserts cover about a third of Earth's landmasses. The largest hot desert is the Saharan in northern Africa.

Deserts are not empty! They have biological diversity of both plants and animals, but the species are limited by the amount of water available, and by extreme temperatures.

DESERT SUPERBLOOM

A superbloom happens when an unusually wet rainy season provides enough water that many wildflowers bloom at about the same time. Desert lands that are normally dry and full of muted colors become brilliant with an array of colorful wildflowers. The life cycle of desert plants relies upon long dormant periods waiting for rain followed by rapid growth right after a rain. Within a week or ten days, plants must sprout, grow, mature, and produce seeds. Whenever a wet season occurs, the cycle repeats.

SPADEFOOT TOAD – A Desert Life Cycle

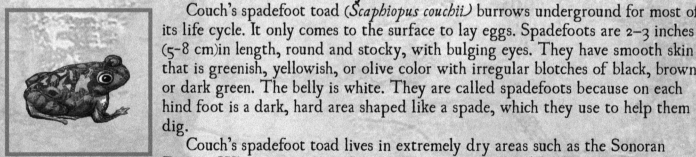

Couch's spadefoot toad (*Scaphiopus couchii*) burrows underground for most of its life cycle. It only comes to the surface to lay eggs. Spadefoots are 2–3 inches (5–8 cm)in length, round and stocky, with bulging eyes. They have smooth skin that is greenish, yellowish, or olive color with irregular blotches of black, brown, or dark green. The belly is white. They are called spadefoots because on each hind foot is a dark, hard area shaped like a spade, which they use to help them dig.

Couch's spadefoot toad lives in extremely dry areas such as the Sonoran Desert. When it rains, an adult female spadefoot (LEFT, TOP) digs to the surface to lay up to 3,000 eggs in small, temporary ponds. In just 9–14 days, the spadefoot will mature from egg to tadpole (LEFT, BOTTOM) to adult.

Adults eat beetles, grasshoppers, katydids, ants, spiders, termites and other insects. As the rains end, they eat a huge meal before they return to burrows to sleep until the next rainy season.

Their call is a low-pitched "waaah," repeated at short intervals. Some people think spadefoot toads smell like peanut butter.

DESERT ANIMALS Find these animals in the story.

Almost every type of animal can be found in a desert habitat. Desert animal species must be able to deal with the heat or cold, and mangage their need for water. Water strategies include getting water from food, storing water in their bodies, or living underground where there's more moisture. Heat strategies may be lighter color skin or fur, which won't absorb as much heat. Sometimes, desert animals have longer ears, legs, or wings giving more surface area for evaporation, which cools them off. They may sleep during the day and only come out at night.

CHUCKWALLA
Sauromalus

COYOTE
Canis latrans

DIAMONDBACK RATTLESNAKE
Crotalus atrox

ELF OWL
Micrathene whitneyi

KANGAROO RAT
Dipodomys

PALLID BAT
Antrozous pallidus

PIPEVINE SWALLOWTAIL
Battus philenor

PUMA
Puma concolor

SCORPION
Scorpiones

GAMBEL'S QUAIL
Callipepla gambelii

AMERICAN DESERTS

The United States has four major desert areas, three hot and one cold.

Chihuahuan Desert—Hot. It lies in the southwestern United States and northcentral Mexico.

Mojave Desert—Hot. It lies in southeastern California and southern Nevada.

Sonoran Desert—Hot. It lies in the southwestern United States and northwest Mexico.

The Great Basin—Cold. It lies mostly in Nevada and Utah.

ARROYO LUPINE
Lupinus succulentus

BARREL CACTUS
Echinocactus grusonii

DESERT PENSTEMON
Penstemon pseudospectabilis

MEXICAN POPPY
Argemone mexicana

ORANGE GLOBE MALLOW
Sphaeralcea munroana

ORGAN PIPE CACTUS
Stenocereus thurberi

OWL'S CLOVER
Castilleja exserta

PRICKLY PEAR
Opuntia

SAGUARO CACTUS
Carnegiea gigantea

SEGO LILY
Calochortus nuttallii

DESERT PLANTS

Find these plants in the story.

Like desert animals, desert plants must be able to deal with the heat or cold and manage their need for water. Most desert species can tolerate dry conditions more easily than non-desert species. A plant may store water, its seeds may stay dormant until enough rainfall occurs, or its leaves may be covered with a waxy substance that prevents evaporation.

READ MORE
Desert Musuem—desertmuseum.org
National Park Service—www.nps.gov/subjects/deserts/index.htm

SCAN ME

CPSIA information can be obtained
at www.ICGtesting.com
Printed in the USA
BVHW012239100223
658310BV00005B/39